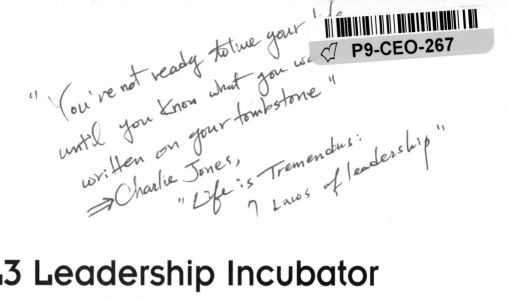

" You're not ready to live your life
until you know what you wa
written on your tombstone "
⟹ Charlie Jones,
" Life is Tremendus :
7 Laws of leadership "

L3 Leadership Incubator
Guidebook

Rodney Smothers,
↗ rtsmothers @ gmail.com

L3 Leadership Incubator Guidebook

Barry Carpenter

Craig Kennet Miller

Craig Robertson

Discipleship Resources
2005

Cover design by Christa Schoenbrodt, interior design by PerfecType, Nashville, TN.

ISBN 0-88177-438-3
Library of Congress Control Number 2004114306

DR438

Contents

Introduction to the Leadership Incubator   1
Session One: Orientation   9

The Personal Vitality Indicator

Session Two: Covenant   17
Session Three: Core   21
Session Four: Call   25
Session Five: Competencies   29
Session Six: Character   33

Incubator Ministry Action Plan (I-MAP)

Team *team .*

Session Seven: Spiritual Life of the Leaders *• prayer*   41
Session Eight: An Environment of Prayer   45
Session Nine: Living as Team *| knowing each other's gifts.*   49
Session Ten: Steps to Team Building *• build as team and live as team*   53

Context *context*

⇒ focus on values
vision
mission

Session Eleven: The Third Place *• understanding of Church*   57
Session Twelve: The Experience-Based Culture *• lifecycle of Church*   61
Session Thirteen: Lifecycle of the Church   65
Session Fourteen: Assessment Results *• Ministry assessment (internal & external)*   69

Vision *Focus*

Session Fifteen: Vision Overview   73
Session Sixteen: Congregational Values *Focus on values, vision, mission.*   79
Session Seventeen: Vision & Mission   83
Session Eighteen: Sustaining the Vision   87

Strategy *Strategy*

Session Nineteen: Introduction to Strategy & Systems   91
Session Twenty: Measurement *• understanding System*   95
Session Twenty-One: Priorities *• measurement*   99
Session Twenty-Two: Structure   103
Session Twenty-Three: Structure & Systems Review *priorities*   107
Session Twenty-Four: Multiplication & Evaluation   111

Relational connections

Implementation Sessions

Session Twenty-Five: Implementation 117
Session Twenty-Six: Implementation 119
Session Twenty-Seven: Implementation 121
Session Twenty-Eight: Implementation 123
Session Twenty-Nine: Implementation 125
Session Thirty: Implementation 127

Transformation

• implementation

• management .

Introduction to the Leadership Incubator

How we are formed affects we way we lead. Most of us grew up with a lecture model through which an expert in a particular field would give us the benefit of his or her research and wisdom. Furiously taking notes we would distill the information in a way that allowed us to pass a test, write a paper, or prepare a document to share with the church council.

The fundamental flaw in this methodology is that it produces people who work in isolation. Rather than being shaped and supported by a community of fellow learners on the journey, it boxes people into the belief that they have to do it on their own. The issue for most of us is not a lack of information. We are one Google click away from finding out the names of the twelve disciples or downloading information about the latest worship experience used by the most creative church of the moment. Most of us who are in leadership positions, whether it be the pastor of a church, the head of the church council, or a denominational leader, would agree that we are information rich but relationship poor.

The results of this approach are easy to see. Pastors who are caught up in the belief that they have to do it all themselves find they are living with a loss of purpose, a defeatist attitude, a lack of trust, and a profound sense of loneliness. Church members who say yes to serving in leadership positions many times find they are working by themselves and soon burn out. Rather than be inspired to do more they look for a way to get out. Denominational leaders who were excited about making great change face low clergy morale, declining budgets, and a profound sense of inadequacy.

A group of twelve leaders in Kentucky gathered together out of conviction that they were the ones who had to change. They concluded their problems were not the fault of denominational leaders, church committees, or congregational members. They acknowledged that their dreams and hopes for their ministry had been allowed to die. Most of them realized they were undeveloped leaders who were not leading anywhere close to their capacity, gifts, or potential. They had become accustomed to blaming their fruitlessness on their congregations or had found creative ways to blame location, spiritual climate, or changing demographics as the root causes of their dormant situations. Most tellingly, they believed there had to be a better way to learn to become leaders.

As they learned to love God more deeply and committed to an ongoing process of peer-to-peer learning, they discovered they could become effective leaders. They learned how to rekindle in the hearts of key leaders a deep love of God. They became leaders who are now agents of transformation in their communities and congregations.

It was out of this experience that The L^3 Leadership Incubator was born. The L^3 Leadership Incubator has at its core a simple idea, "iron sharpens iron." What does this exactly mean? Although a few people are born leaders, most people become leaders by being in community with other leaders.

Rodney Smothers, who has served in many leadership roles in the church, and is the Director of Congregational Development of the Baltimore-Washington Annual Conference, says this about his Incubator experience, "It promotes a supportive community where people encourage one another, stretch one another, and hold one another accountable. It literally is life transforming because you come through the other side of the process having discovered your unrealized potential."

D. Max Whitfield, Resident Bishop Northwest Texas/New Mexico Area of The United Methodist Church, who, with his cabinet, participated in an Incubator, was excited to see that people of different theological identities were able to find common ground as they prayed and supported each other and followed a process that allowed them to develop a new strategy for their ministry.

The L³ Leadership Incubator offers a radical proposition: leaders are formed in community with other leaders. This community has a few essential characteristics:

1. They hold each other to a higher level of accountability.

2. They create an environment of trust, innovation, and action.

3. They develop a process that transforms their congregations into disciple-making faith communities.

If this sounds familiar, it is. Check out the leadership development strategy of Jesus. For three years he invested his time and energy in the lives of twelve disciples. Yes, he preached to the crowds and he taught the seventy, but his main purpose was to transplant God's vision of a new kingdom on earth into the hearts and minds of twelve people whom the world saw as simpleminded fishermen, scandalous tax collectors, thieves, and terrorists. Yet, as funny as it may seem, it was this single-minded pursuit of Jesus to turn this rabble into leaders that eventually changed the world.

Or what about the so-called "Holy Club," the initial "Incubator" of the Methodist movement in England? Almost on a dare, Charles Wesley and his buddies at Oxford started praying together, took communion daily, and served the poor. When his brother John Wesley joined them, they took it up a notch and became known as Methodists because of their unwavering pursuit of God and service to the poor and downtrodden. Out of that initial group, a spiritual movement was born that transformed the face of England and gave birth to a Christian movement that encircles the world.

Most Christian movements and denominations have at their roots a small band of believers who committed themselves to God and to one another. Out of this new environment they created new ways to share the gospel and new structures to implement their heart-felt convictions and spiritual practices.

An Invitation

The goal of the L³ Leadership Incubator is to create an environment in which spiritual leaders and ideas are born, nurtured, and developed. As a member of an Incubator you will join with six to eleven others who are committed to deepening their faith in Jesus Christ and creating ways to multiply their effectiveness and their ministry.

The purpose of the Incubator is threefold:

First, to resource and encourage you as a leader. One of the first things you will do with your Incubator is to form a covenant around your life together. Critical to this covenant will be your willingness to be in prayer and support for others.

Second, to learn how to create and sustain Incubators in your congregation and in your area. One of the most exciting aspects of the Incubator is the multiplication factor. This is not a one-time thing. We see this as being a valuable tool for you to use to multiply your ministry.

Third, to create a disciple-making faith community. A congregation becomes a disciple-making faith community when it develops an intentional process for welcoming newcomers, introduces them to faith in Jesus Christ, helps them discover God's call in their life, and sends them out for the transformation of the world. All aspects of congregational life, including worship, Christian formation, and community service, work together with a common goal of creating an environment where people find faith in Jesus Christ and who, in turn, are equipped to be Christian leaders in their churches, communities, and families.

Each participant in an Incubator is challenged to:

1. Be in covenant with your L³ Leadership Incubator

2. Become a team leader and start other Incubators

3. Develop an Incubator Ministry Action Plan (I-MAP)

One of the lessons that we are learning is that true change takes time. As a member of an Incubator you will join in a journey of faith and discovery as you commit to gather with a group of fellow believers over the course of the next eighteen months.

The L³ Principle

Since its initial start in Kentucky, L³ Leadership Incubators have been started among a number of different groups: New Church Pastors, Turnaround Pastors, Hispanic Pastors, Bishops and Cabinets, and national Incubators made up of people from around the country. One idea they have had in common is the L³ Principle.

The L³ Principle is the template for every Incubator experience. L¹ symbolizes loving God and neighbor. A leader's credentials for leading others to transformation is based on his or her personal relationship with the living Christ and the power that emanates from this bond of love. Loving God is our highest calling and sharing that love with others is our highest passion. The primary purpose of an L³ Leadership Incubator is to nurture and provoke the leader's personal love of God and neighbor.

L² is learning. Leadership is directly related to continual learning and sharing. No one person knows it all. Today those who are in a learning community are best poised to benefit from what is working in other churches and to learn how to apply the best practices found in business, non-profits, and government. The Incubator is designed to be a learning think tank, where people learn to lead with integrity and innovation.

L³ is leading. The practices associated with leadership today are vastly different from those just twenty years ago. Communication techniques, cultural awareness, organizational constructs, and technological advances are just a few of the disciplines that have an impact on leadership in the context of this generation.

Disciple-Making Faith Community

A congregation becomes a disciple-making faith community when it develops an intentional process for welcoming newcomers, introduces them to faith in Jesus Christ, helps them discover God's call for their life, and sends them out for the transformation of the world. All aspects of congregational life, including worship, Christian formation, and community service, work together with a common goal of creating an environment where people find faith in Jesus Christ and who, in turn, are equipped to be Christian leaders in their churches, communities, and families.

The Incubator Process

During the course of eighteen months, an Incubator will meet in blocks of four-hour sessions. Some Incubators meet twice a month for four hours at a time, while others meet once a month for eight hours. If some participants are traveling long distances, some will meet over the course of two days. The first day they meet in the afternoon, stay overnight, and meet in the morning of the second day.

As the Incubator moves through the year it goes through six different phases. Each phase has tools to help participants move through the process.

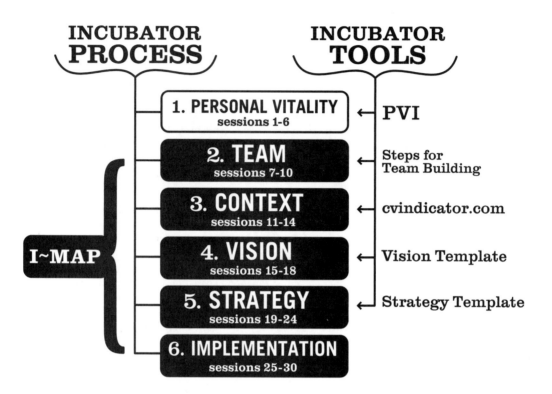

Phase One is Personal Vitality. During the first six sessions, participants will focus on their personal spiritual growth and leadership. Topics such as covenant, call, core, competencies, and character will be covered as participants fill out their Personal Vitality Indicator (PVI), which is the tool for this phase. The PVI is a template that participants use to look at their leadership skills, characteristics, and gifts. It guides them through a series of questions and enables them to develop a picture of their spiritual life and their leadership profile. It also helps them self-identify their strengths and weaknesses so that as they develop a leadership team, they can find people whose gifts and abilities complement theirs.

Phase Two begins the process of using the Incubator Ministry Action Plan (I-MAP). The five points of the I-MAP are Team, Context, Vision, Strategy, and Implementation. Phase Two's tool, Steps for Team Building, teaches how to build teams that take into account the talents and abilities of all the team members as they work together to accomplish a shared task.

Phase Three is developing a portrait of the Context of the congregation and community. Demographics, assessment of a congregation's context in the community, and listening are key ingredients for getting a clear picture of a congregation's current reality. The tool for this phase is found at www.cvindicator.com, a website designed to help a congregation get a clear picture of its current congregational life and relationship to the community—its current reality. Tips and tools for assessing demographics, congregational life, and listening are included on the site. Churches that purchase the L³ Leadership Incubator Kit are given a one year trial of the www.cvindicator.com. After one year, an annual fee allows a congregation to continue to use its web-based resources.

One of the most powerful tools on the site is the Church Vitality Indicator (CVI). Rather than focusing on strengths or weaknesses, it asks a more important question: what is the key driver, that area which has the most influence over the whole ministry of the congregation, of your church? By working through a series of questions clustered around twenty-two church vitality indicators, leaders are able to determine where to focus their energy in a way that gives them the most results.

What makes the CVI unique is that serves multiple purposes:

It has a holistic approach that makes it usable by a variety of congregational types and sizes.

It is an easy-to-use, online, password-protected questionnaire that gives instant, graphic results through its web-based database.

It invites leaders to engage in a process of discernment over key areas of congregational life.

It serves as an educational tool that teaches the congregation about what makes a church vital.

It creates a leading edge priority chart from the questionnaire that gives a congregation a clear picture of what it is already doing well and where to use its time and resources most effectively.

It links leaders to resources that give guidelines for how to improve in twenty-two areas of church vitality.

Phase Four, Vision, uses the Vision Template, which helps a congregation incorporate its context, values, and mission into a clearly articulated vision for the future.

Phase Five is the development of an effective Strategy for putting the vision into action by building efficient systems and structures that are able to multiply ministries. The Strategy Template is a powerful tool for developing an effective system that takes into account all aspects of congregational life.

Phase Six is the Implementation of the I-MAP, which enables congregations to be disciple-making faith communities.

The Incubator Session

Each Incubator session follows the same simple format. The first two hours focus on L^1: Loving, where participants gather for **Incubate Your Heart** and for their **Formation Que**. For most Incubators this accountability and sharing time is the most fruitful. As people share their struggles and successes, a community of support and encouragement helps them move to a higher level of spiritual maturity and leadership growth.

The second two hours focus on L^2: Learning and L^3: Leading. The first part of this time is spent on **Reflection**. Participants will review what they have learned from their last session and will report what they learned since the last time they met. For example, if the previous session was on congregational prayer, during the reflection time they will share what they learned about their church's system of congregational prayer.

Next, participants focus on the **Key Concept**. Using the presentation slides on the DVD, participants learn the critical Incubator principles for this session. The final component is the **Assignment**, which participants are to complete before the next session.

Components of the L³ Leadership Incubator Kit

The L^3 Leadership Incubator Kit has everything you need to start an Incubator in your church. The components are as follows:

1. Six L³ Leadership Incubator Guidebooks

   As you look through the guidebook you will see lesson plans for each session. This resource will give you all the information you need to participate in an Incubator and to lead an Incubator group in the future.

2. L³ Leadership Incubator Multi-media Pack

   - The multi-media pack contains a DVD that will be used during your first twenty-four sessions. Each of the twenty-four sessions has the following:
   - A worship experience called **Incubate Your Heart** with music and lyrics for each song.
   - Presentation slides for the leader's use to guide the participants through the Key Concept material for that session.

3. Access to the www.L3incubator.com and www.cvindicator.com websites

   - The L³ Leadership Incubator website (www.L3incubator.com) has suggested helps for each session and presentation scripts for the leader to use as he or she leads each session.
   - The www.cvindicator.com site has tools for understanding the context of your congregation and for discovering its vital indicators for fruitful ministry. This is where you will find the Church Vitality Indicator (CVI).

4. Startup pamphlet that answers questions like, "What is an Incubator?" "Why would I want to start one?" "Where do I begin if I'm a pastor?" "How do I get a group together?" "What equipment do I need?" "How much preparation time will I need to invest?" and "How do I use the CVI?"

Facilitation Tips

Each session follows a basic pattern. On the first page of each session you will find Today's Outline. On the left-hand column you will find the lesson plan for the day with a suggested time allotted for each component. On the right you will find where the material you will need is located.

For example, here is the outline for **Session Four: Call**.

The session begins with **Incubate Your Heart** on the theme of "Two Calls," with a recommended time of thirty minutes. To lead this session you will use DVD 1 and go to **Incubate Your Heart**. After **Incubate Your Heart**, you will use the **Formation Que**, which is in the Incubator Guidebook. Typically, this lasts ninety minutes.

As you move into L²: **Learn** you will use the **Reflection** template, which is printed in the Incubator Guidebook to discuss last session's **Key Concept**, which, in this case, is "Core." Typically this will take about forty-five minutes.

Next you will spend approximately sixty minutes on this session's **Key Concept**, "Call." You will use DVD 1 and go to Session 4 on "Call." If you are the person who will lead this session for the group, you will need to go to www.L3incubator.com some time prior to the session and download the session notes for "Session Four: Call." The session notes will give you the ideas and instructions on how to share the **Key Concept**.

Finally, you will conclude the session by moving into L³: **Lead** by looking over the **Assignment** on "Your Call." Participants will be expected to work through this material in preparation for the next session.

Today's Outline		What You Need to Lead
L¹: Love		
Incubate Your Heart (30 min.)	Two Calls	**DVD: Session Four**
Formation Que (90 min.)		**Incubator Guidebook**
L²: Learn		
Reflection (45 min.)	Core	**Incubator Guidebook**
Key Concept (60 min.)	Call	**DVD: Session Four**
		www.L3incubator.com
		Session Notes on Session Four
L³: Lead		
Assignment (15 min.)	Your Call	**Incubator Guidebook**

For more ideas on how to lead each session, go to the Incubator website, www.L3incubator.com, which will give you pointers about leading an Incubator and additional resources you can use with your group.

During the first six sessions you will be building your Personal Vitality Indicator. The rest of the sessions are devoted to developing your I-MAP.

Explanation of Terms Used Throughout the Guidebook

The Transformation Triangle

Transformation occurs when:

Leadership changes and rises to lead with new expectations before they expect others to change.

An environment of love and trust is created.

A process to learn how to change is developed and implemented.

Formation Que (Question)

Every Incubator session starts out by focusing on the spiritual vitality and formation of its participants. After a time of worship, the Incubator turns its attention to the Formation Que. The Formation Que (question) is a covenantal question that all L³ Incubator participants agree to answer and be accountable for each time the Incubator meets. The question each person is asked to respond to is, "What will I do to live in full devotion to Jesus Christ?"

As participants reflect and share around the Formation Que they become part of an environment of trust and support that encourages each person to mature in his or her spiritual life.

Fulcrum Leaders

A fulcrum leader is a person of influence whose conduct and initiative influences others. Rather than leading by virtue of position, a fulcrum leader leads by developing a web of influence. Through personal interaction, relationship building, and mentoring, he or she is able to change the attitudes of others and create environments of encouragement and spiritual formation. One of the goals of the Incubator is to help participants become fulcrum leaders.

Fulcrum Congregations

Fulcrum congregations sense a call to effect change in the Christian movement. They develop systems that are reproducible, transferable, and credible. They are centers of learning and innovation for congregations and the world.

Intentionality

The principle of intentionality says that 1) we need others to keep us accountable for spiritual growth and that 2) in order to move a congregation from one place to another, a plan needs to be developed, implemented, and periodically evaluated. It is not enough to *believe* a change needs to be made in our lives. We must develop a plan for change and *act* upon it. This is as true for personal spiritual growth as it is for developing a vital congregation.

Multiplication

One of the guiding principles of the Incubator is that effective leaders reproduce effective leaders. Leaders who create vital congregations learn how to discover, develop, and deploy passionate spiritual leaders.

This same principle applies to the reproduction of Incubators themselves. Once a group of leaders experience an Incubator, they are then to start another Incubator.

Typically an Incubator will be formed with a group of pastoral leaders in a particular geographic area. They could be a group of new church pastors, or turnaround pastors, pastors of particular sized congregations, or pastors who share a particular cultural distinctiveness, like language or ethnicity.

Somewhere between the sixth and twelfth month, each person is to start an Incubator in his or her congregation with a group of key leaders. These key leaders, in turn, will be encouraged to start Incubators in particular ministry areas like worship or Christian education.

Session One

Orientation

Now to him who by the power at work within us is able to accomplish abundantly far more than all we can ask or imagine, to him be glory in the church and in Christ Jesus to all generations, forever and ever. Amen.
EPHESIANS 3:20-21

Today's Outline

L¹: Love
Incubate Your Heart (30 min.)

L²: Learn
Key Concept (60 min.)

Reflection (45 min.)
L³ Overview (75 min.)

L³: Lead
Assignment (15 min.)

The Real Me

The Path to
Transformation
Leadership
L³ Overview

What You Need to Lead

DVD: Session One

Session Notes for Session One
www.L3incubator.com

Incubator Guidebook

Incubator Guidebook

Key Concept

The Path to Transformation

- Leadership must change and rise to lead with new expectations before we expect others to change (PVI)

- An environment of love and trust must be created (Incubator)

- A process to learn how to change must be developed (I-MAP)

Reflection

FOUR BY FOUR (30 MINUTES)

Divide into groups of four and discuss this question: What do you believe are your possibilities as a leader?

Write down some of your reflections as you share with one another.

_____

_____

_____

_____

_____

GROUP LEARNING (15 MINUTES)

Write down what you have learned about being a leader from listening to the group.

_____
_____
_____
_____
_____
_____

L³ Overview

What do participants in Incubators do?

1. They commit to learning together over the course of eighteen months.

2. In loving support, they hold each other accountable for spiritual growth, personal piety, and leadership development.

3. They give themselves to God in worship, prayer, and Christian conversation.

4. They learn a process that will teach them how to transform their congregations into disciple-making faith communities.

The L³ Leadership Incubator is an environment where leaders and ideas are born, nurtured, and developed.

L¹ stands for loving: Loving God and neighbor.

L² stands for learning. We learn together as we understand our personal gifts and abilities, as we investigate the current reality of our context and congregations, and as we plan for the future.

L³ stands for leading. We lead by implementing an Incubator Ministry Action Plan with others.

The Formation Que (question) is a covenantal question that all L³ Incubator participants agree to answer and be held accountable to each time the Incubator meets. The question each person is asked to respond to is, "What will I do to live in full devotion to Jesus Christ?" At our next session we will participate in the Formation Que for the first time.

Assignment

Go to www.L3incubator.com and pick one of the books from the suggested reading list to read before the next session.

Read about the Personal Vitality Indicator on pages 15–16.

Do a study of one of your favorite leaders in the Bible and look for these aspects of his or her life:

Covenant
Core
Call
Competencies
Character

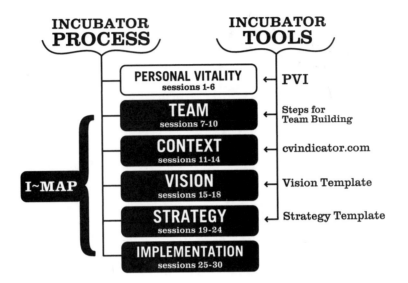

Spiritual life.
physical health
relationships
work

Principle of Multiplication

The genius of the Incubator is that it is designed to be reproduced.

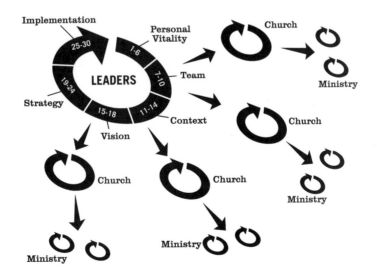

"Covenant": meaning
- Koinonia
- a shared dream / compelling purpose

→ metaphors   circumcision
   gardens   the Ark of Covenant .
   flames

   dove
   rainbow

The Personal Vitality Indicator

What action/s do I intend to take
that enhances my relationship
with Jesus Christ that results
in the life of Christlike?

During the next five sessions you will focus on your own spiritual development and leadership quotient. Before we can focus on developing a strategy or work to grow the spiritual life of a congregation, its leadership must be committed to God. Those in leadership need to remember that their strength, hope, and compassion are dependent on their relationship to Jesus Christ.

John Wesley's covenant prayer is a great reminder that our most reliable and powerful source is found in our connection to God:

I am no longer my own, but thine.
Put me to what thou wilt, rank me with whom thou wilt.
Put me to doing, put me to suffering.
Let me be employed by thee or laid aside for thee,
exalted for thee or brought low for thee.
Let me be full, let me be empty.
Let me have all things, let me have nothing.
I freely and heartily yield all things
to thy pleasure and disposal.
And now, O glorious and blessed God,
Father, Son, and Holy Spirit,
thou art mine, and I am thine. So be it.
And the covenant which I have made on earth,
let it be ratified in heaven. **Amen.**

> *The United Methodist Hymnal* (Nashville, TN: The United Methodist Publishing House, 1989), 607.

The Personal Vitality Indicator focuses on five key components of vital leadership:

1. Covenant – your connection to God and others

2. Core – your motivation, identity, direction, and values

3. Call – God's call for your life

4. Competencies – your passion, gifts, talents, and abilities

5. Character – your personality, spiritual type, and worldview

As you move through these sessions you will be invited to fill out the Personal Vitality Indicator (PVI). The PVI is a template that you will use to find your leadership profile. As you work through this process you will find your greatest strengths and weaknesses. As you do so you will begin to discern whom you need to have in your leadership core that enhances, builds on, and adds onto your leadership profile. Great leaders surround themselves with people who are much better than they in key areas of congregational life. To live into this principle you first must spend some time discovering who you are as a leader as you share your insights, dilemmas, passions, and dreams with your Incubator. As it says in Proverbs 27:17-19:

[17] Iron sharpens iron,
    and one person sharpens the wits of another.
[18] Anyone who tends a fig tree will eat its fruit,
    and anyone who takes care of a master will be honored.
[19] Just as water reflects the face,
    so one human heart reflects another.

Personal Vitality Indicator

Covenant

With whom are you in a covenant relationship?

Core

Center: What is central in your life?
Objective: What is your goal? What do you want to be remembered for?
Relationships: With whom are you in relationship?
Ethos: How do you think people see you?

Call

As you look over your life's journey, where do you see God's influence?
In what direction is God calling you to go today?
Who is God calling you to be?

Competencies

Identify your Passion
Investigate your Gifts
Improve your Serve
Increase your Skills

Character

What are your personality traits?
What is your spiritual type?
What experiences have shaped who you are today?
What are your greatest strengths and weaknesses?
Who do you need on your team?

Session Two

Covenant

Then he took a loaf of bread, and when he had given thanks, he broke it and gave it to them, saying, "This is my body, which is given for you. Do this in remembrance of me." And he did the same with the cup after supper, saying, "This cup that is poured out for you is the new covenant in my blood." LUKE 22:19-20

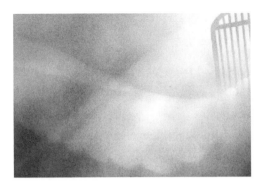

Today's Outline		What You Need to Lead
L¹: Love		
Incubate Your Heart (30 min.)	**Covenant Leadership**	**DVD: Session Two**
Formation Que (90 min.)		**Incubator Guidebook**
L²: Learn		
Key Concept (60 min.)	**Covenant**	**DVD: Session Two**
		www.L3incubator.com
		Session Notes for Session Two
Reflection (45 min.)	**Group Covenant**	**Incubator Guidebook**
L³: Lead		
Assignment (15 min.)		**Incubator Guidebook**

Formation Que

The covenantal question or questions that all L³ Incubator participants agree to answer and be accountable to each time the Incubator meets.

(List names of your Incubator participants below)

_____

_____

_____

_____

_____

_____

_____

_____

_____

_____

_____

"What will I do to live in full devotion to Jesus Christ?"

(List responses below)

_____

_____

_____

_____

_____

_____

_____

_____

_____

_____

_____

Key Concept

Covenant

Covenant is the foundation of partnerships. Partnerships are the basis for ministry. Leadership is about forming partnerships and transmitting God's vision to others.

These four questions form the basis of our covenant:

What does a spiritual leader look like?

What does a spiritual team look like?

What are the non-negotiables of our relationship?

What is the desired outcome of this relationship?

DVD Notes

_____
_____
_____
_____
_____
_____

Reflection

Guidelines for building a covenant for an L³ Leadership Incubator:

1. This covenant will guide our relationships for the duration of this Incubator.

2. Once it is agreed upon by everyone, it cannot be changed except by consent of the whole group.

3. At the next session it will be printed out so that each person may sign it.

4. Any changes to the number of people who participate in the Incubator need to be agreed upon by all participants.

Develop a covenant agreement among yourselves that addresses these questions:

1. What does a great leader look like?

2. What does a great team look like?

3. What are the non-negotiables of our relationships in this Incubator?

4. What is the desired outcome of these relationships in our Incubator?

5. What are the participation expectations for your Incubator?

  • Attendance at sessions

  • Preparation before each session

  • Other

6. How often will you be in prayer for one another?

  • Daily

  • Weekly

  • Other

7. Incubator non-negotiables:

  • Confidentiality

  • How much time will people have to share?

  • Acceptance of different points of view

  • Other

8. What happens if we breach the covenant?

Assignment

Personal Vitality Indicator

Answer the following:

1. What is the difference between my connections and covenant relationships? (Connections are people with whom we are in relationship. Covenantal relationships are based on mutual agreement.)

_____

_____

_____

2. Who am I in covenant with?

_____

_____

_____

3. What covenants and connections do I need to develop?

_____

_____

_____

Session Three

Core

In the same way, every good tree bears good fruit, but the bad tree bears bad fruit. A good tree cannot bear bad fruit, nor can a bad tree bear good fruit. MATTHEW 7:17-18

Today's Outline		What You Need to Lead
L¹: Love		
Incubate Your Heart (30 min.)	**Bearing Fruit**	**DVD: Session Three** (bring communion elements)
Formation Que (90 min.)		**Incubator Guidebook**
L²: Learn		
Reflection (45 min.)	**Review your Covenant**	**Incubator Guidebook**
Key Concept (60 min.)	**Core**	**DVD: Session Three** www.L3incubator.com **Session Notes for Session Three**
L³: Lead		
Assignment (15 min.)	**PVI**	**Incubator Guidebook**

Formation Que

The covenantal question or questions that all L³ Incubator participants agree to answer and be accountable to each time the Incubator meets.

"What will I do to live in full devotion to Jesus Christ?"

(List names of your Incubator participants below)

(List responses below)

_____

_____

_____

_____

_____

_____

_____

_____

_____

_____

_____

Reflection

Review the covenant you made last time.

_____

_____

_____

After reviewing, have the group sign the covenant.

End with prayer.

Key Concept

Core

What is at your core?

Center: What is central in your life?
*Why are you doing what you are doing? This question addresses the issue of **motivation**.*

Objective: What is your goal? What do you want to be remembered for?
*Who do you think you are? This addresses our **direction**. How you see yourself determines your outcome.*

Relationships: With whom are you in relationship?
*What is the quality of your relationships? This question addresses the issue of **identity**.*

Ethos: How do you think people see you?
*What do they say about your character? What do you think is so important? This addresses the issue of **values**.*

DVD Notes

_____

_____

_____

_____

_____

Assignment

Before the next session think deeply about your life and answer the following:

Center: What is central in your life? *Why are you doing what you are doing?*

_____

_____

_____

Objective: What is your goal? What do you want to be remembered for? *Who do you think you are?*

_____

_____

_____

Relationships: With whom are you in relationship? *What is the quality of your relationships?*

_____

_____

_____

Ethos: How do you think people see you? *What do they say about your character?*

_____

_____

_____

Session Four

Call

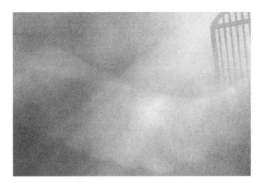

As he walked by the Sea of Galilee, he saw two brothers, Simon, who is called Peter, and Andrew his brother, casting a net into the sea—for they were fishermen. And he said to them, "Follow me, and I will make you fish for people." MATTHEW 4:18-19

When they had finished breakfast, Jesus said to Simon Peter, "Simon son of John, do you love me more than these?" He said to him, "Yes, Lord; you know that I love you." Jesus said to him, "Feed my lambs." JOHN 21:15

Today's Outline

L¹: Love
Incubate Your Heart (30 min.)   Follow me X2
Formation Que (90 min.)

L²: Learn
Reflection (45 min.)   Core
Key Concept (60 min.)   Call

L³: Lead
Assignment (15 min.)

What You Need to Lead

DVD: Session Four
Incubator Guidebook

Incubator Guidebook
DVD: Session Four
www.L3incubator.com
Session Notes for Session Four

Incubator Guidebook

Formation Que

The covenantal question or questions that all L³ Incubator participants agree to answer and be accountable to each time the Incubator meets.

"What will I do to live in full devotion to Jesus Christ?"

(List names of your Incubator participants below)

(List responses below)

Reflection

FOUR BY FOUR (30 MINUTES)

Divide into groups of four and share what you learned about yourself from the last session on core values.

Write down some of your reflections as you share with one another.

_____
_____
_____

GROUP LEARNING (15 MINUTES)

What are you learning about the importance of core values?

_____
_____
_____

Write down what you have learned about Core from listening to the group.

_____
_____
_____
_____
_____
_____
_____

Key Concept

Call

God has created us for a purpose, which we live out when we follow God's call in our life. Call can be lived out in many ways. Family, vocation, community service, and ministry through the Church are just some of the settings where we live out our call. God's call is twofold, to follow and to serve.

1. Conversion call
   "Follow me…"
2. Call to serve
   Baptism call "Witnesses unto me in…"
   Vocation call "Vocation" comes from the Latin word _vocatio_, meaning to
   summon or call. Therefore, a vocation is a calling from God.

DVD Notes

_____
_____
_____
_____
_____

Assignment

Personal Vitality Indicator

Prayerfully answer the following:

As you look over your life's journey, <u>where</u> do you see <u>God's influence</u>?

love, forgiveness . (way of life) — hubris pride (competition in nature)
(humility)

In what direction is God calling you to go today?

labor in love

Who is God calling you to be?

labor in love sacrifice himself

♍ 2:10

Conversion call is a call to worship.
Baptism is a call to obey
Vocation is a call to witness.

Session Five

Competencies

Now there are varieties of gifts, but the same Spirit; and there are varieties of services, but the same Lord; and there are varieties of activities, but it is the same God who activates all of them in everyone. To each is given the manifestation of the Spirit for the common good. 1 CORINTHIANS 12:4-7

Today's Outline		What You Need to Lead
L¹: Love		
Incubate Your Heart (30 min.)	**Rightful Ownership**	**DVD: Session Five**
Formation Que (90 min.)		**Incubator Guidebook**
L²: Learn		
Reflection (45 min.)	**Call**	**Incubator Guidebook**
Key Concept (60 min.)	**Competencies**	**DVD: Session Five**
		www.L3incubator.com
		Session Notes for Session Five
L³: Lead		
Assignment (15 min.)		**Incubator Guidebook**

Formation Que

The covenantal question or questions that all L³ Incubator participants agree to answer and be accountable to each time the Incubator meets.

(List names of your Incubator participants below)

"What will I do to live in full devotion to Jesus Christ?"

(List responses below)

Reflection

FOUR BY FOUR (30 MINUTES)

Divide into groups of four and share what you learned about yourself from the last session on Call.

Write down some of your reflections as you share with one another.

_____

_____

_____

_____

GROUP LEARNING (15 MINUTES)

What are you learning about Call?

_____

_____

_____

Write down what you have learned about Call from listening to the group.

_____

_____

_____

_____

_____

Key Concept

Competencies

Leadership is taking people to a place they would not go without you. In order to do that we must either have or develop the competencies to influence, inform, inspire, and initiate change that results in reconciliation and transformation. God has blessed you by grace with natural and supernatural competencies:

1. Innate skills and competencies (Grace Endowments)
2. Competencies designed to assist the community of Christ (Grace Gifts)

Every gift is from God, who desires to channel his energy and power as a means of strengthening the body of Christ and bringing glory to his name!

There are personal, interpersonal, and professional skills that are needed to faithfully equip the whole Church.

DVD Notes

_____

_____

_____

_____

_____

_____

Assignment

Personal Vitality Indicator

As you answer the following, think about your spiritual gifts, leadership skills, and personal abilities. (Go to www.L3incubator.com for a listing of online resources you can use for looking at abilities and spiritual gifts.)

Identify your Passion: What gets you going?

_____

_____

_____

_____

Investigate your Gifts: What are your spiritual gifts?

_____

_____

_____

_____

Improve your Serve: Where are you using your gifts?

_____

_____

_____

_____

Increase your Skills: What skills do you have? What do you need to increase your effectiveness?

_____

_____

_____

_____

Session Six

Character QUALITY PERSONALITY (RELIABLE, HONEST)

A good name is to be chosen rather than great riches,
and favor is better than silver or gold.
The rich and the poor have this in common:
the LORD is the maker of them all. PROVERBS 22:1-2

By contrast, the fruit of the Spirit is love, joy, peace, patience, kindness, generosity, faithfulness, gentleness, and self-control. There is no law against such things. GALATIANS 5:22-23

Today's Outline		What You Need to Lead
L¹: Love		
Incubate Your Heart (30 min.)	**Authentic Person**	**DVD: Session Six**
Formation Que (90 min.)		**Incubator Guidebook**
L²: Learn		
Key Concept (60 min.)	**Character**	**DVD: Session Six**
		www.L3incubator.com
		Session Notes for Session Six
Reflection (45 min.)	**Competencies**	**Incubator Guidebook**
L³: Lead		
Assignment (15 min.)		**Incubator Guidebook**

Formation Que

The covenantal question or questions that all L³ Incubator participants agree to answer and be accountable to each time the Incubator meets.

"What will I do to live in full devotion to Jesus Christ?"

(List names of your Incubator participants below)

(List responses below)

_____
_____
_____
_____
_____
_____
_____
_____
_____
_____

_____
_____
_____
_____
_____
_____
_____
_____
_____
_____

Key Concept

Character

Competency is having the skill or ability to do something effectively. Integrity is the quality of adhering to high moral principles or professional standards. If we are competent but lack integrity, we hurt rather than help. If we have character but lack competency, we lack the ability to help people reach their potential.

Character is not a nebulous quality. It can be easily identified and is basic to leading anyone anywhere. Character consists of strengths such as trustworthiness, respect, kindness, responsibility, a love for justice, caring, gratitude, and discipline.

DVD Notes

_____

_____

_____

_____

_____

Reflection

FOUR BY FOUR (30 MINUTES)

Divide into groups of four and share what you learned about yourself from the last session on Competencies.

Write down some of your reflections as you share with one another.

_____

_____

_____

_____

GROUP LEARNING (15 MINUTES)

What are you learning about Competencies?

_____

_____

_____

Write down what you have learned about Competencies from listening to the group.

_____

_____

_____

_____

Assignment

Personal Vitality Indicator

Answer the following:

1. What are your personality traits?

_____
_____
_____
_____

2. What is your spiritual type?

_____
_____
_____
_____

3. Who do you feel comfortable with?

_____
_____
_____
_____

4. What experiences have shaped who you are today?

_____
_____
_____
_____

5. What are your greatest strengths and weaknesses?

_____
_____
_____
_____

6. Who do you need on your team?

_____
_____
_____
_____

Incubator Ministry
Action Plan (I-MAP)

Now that you have completed your PVI, you are ready to look at your congregation. During the rest of the Incubator, you will be developing your strategic plan using the I-MAP. As you work together you will have an opportunity to learn and explore the different steps of a process that will give you the tools and insights you need to set specific goals and develop long-term strategies.

Before you can develop a strategy, you first need to understand the whole process. Thus, the goal is not necessarily to have a whole strategic plan ready to go when you have finished the Incubator. More important is to understand the process and to learn the tools. As you move into this process there are three basic concepts to keep in mind:

1. Strategic planning is a team effort.

   While it may be tempting to develop a strategic plan for your congregation and present it to them, a far more effective approach is to work together with a group of key leaders. If you are going through the L³ Leadership Incubator with a group of pastoral leaders, your goal is to learn the process. Then when you lead an Incubator with a group of leaders in your congregation, together you will develop a strategic plan.

2. A strategy without implementation is a waste of time.

   Many congregations have spent much time and effort on a planning process only to see it fail because they did not think about the steps they needed to take to put it into action.

3. Strategic plans are meant to be changed.

   A good strategic plan allows for flexibility and review. It is open to innovation and the nudging of the Holy Spirit.

Let's review phases of the I-MAP.

Phase One: Creating a **Team** that focuses on spiritual formation, develops a prayer environment, balances gifts and talents, and develops a process for putting gifts into action.

Phase Two: Developing the **Context** of the congregation and community. Assessing the demographics, congregational life, and listening are key ingredients for getting a clear picture of a congregation's current reality.

Phase Three: Defining a **Vision** that incorporates a congregation's context, values, and mission.

Phase Four: Developing an effective **Strategy** for putting the vision into action by building efficient systems and structures that are able to multiply ministries.

Phase Five: **Implementation** of the I-MAP enables congregations to be disciple-making faith communities.

The I-MAP is a process that will move you from **Team** to **Implementation**. Each section has its own set of tools and templates to help you accomplish your goal of creating disciple-making faith communities.

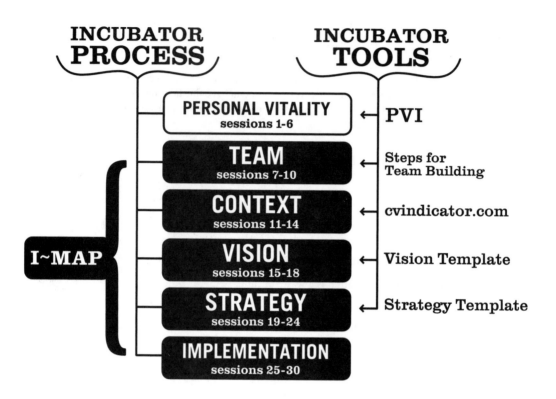

INCUBATOR
PROCESS

INCUBATOR
TOOLS

I~MAP

PERSONAL VITALITY
sessions 1-6
← PVI

TEAM
sessions 7-10
← Steps for
Team Building

CONTEXT
sessions 11-14
← cvindicator.com

VISION
sessions 15-18
← Vision Template

STRATEGY
sessions 19-24
← Strategy Template

IMPLEMENTATION
sessions 25-30

Session Seven

Spiritual Life of the Leaders

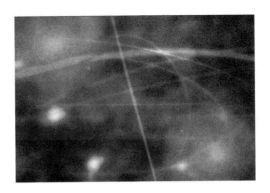

Let us hold fast to the confession of our hope without wavering, for he who has promised is faithful. And let us consider how to provoke one another to love and good deeds, not neglecting to meet together, as is the habit of some, but encouraging one another, and all the more as you see the Day approaching. HEBREWS 10:23-25

Today's Outline		What You Need to Lead
L¹: Love **Incubate Your Heart** (30 min.) **Formation Que** (90 min.)	**Marks of a Disciple**	**DVD: Session Seven** **Incubator Guidebook**
L²: Learn **Reflection** (45 min.) **Key Concept** (60 min.)	**Character** **Spiritual Disciplines** **of the Leaders**	**Incubator Guidebook** **DVD: Session Seven** **www.L3incubator.com** **Session Notes for Session Seven**
L³: Lead **Assignment** (15 min.)		**Incubator Guidebook**

Formation Que

The covenantal question or questions that all L³ Incubator participants agree to answer and be accountable to each time the Incubator meets.

(List names of your Incubator participants below)

_____
_____
_____
_____
_____
_____
_____
_____
_____
_____
_____

"What will I do to live in full devotion to Jesus Christ?"

(List responses below)

_____
_____
_____
_____
_____
_____
_____
_____
_____
_____
_____

Reflection

FOUR BY FOUR (30 MINUTES)

Divide into groups of four and share what you learned about yourself from the last session on Character.

Write down some of your reflections as you share with one another.

_____

_____

_____

GROUP LEARNING (15 MINUTES)

What are you learning about Character?

_____

_____

_____

Write down what you have learned about Character from listening to the group.

_____

_____

_____

_____

_____

Key Concept

Spiritual Life of the Leaders

A leader's spiritual life shapes the congregation. The spiritual disciplines and practices they live by and model infuse the whole congregation with a spiritual vitality that is contagious and life-giving.

Jesus' first task was to teach a small band of disciples a way of living. His life was a witness of how to live in relationship with God and with others.

John Wesley and the early Methodists talked about the practice of spiritual disciplines as a way to shape the community of faith. These practices, known as the means of grace, were a way of transforming both individuals and the body of believers. Through the public worship of God, the ministry of the word, The Lord's supper, family and private prayer, searching the scriptures, fasting and abstinence, and Christian conferencing, believers were called to enter a journey of transformation that would move them into deeper communion with Christ and with fellow believers. But this was not enough—they also were called to share their faith with those who did not know Jesus and give to those who were in need. Love of God and neighbor, the worship of God and service to the community, made up the two pinnacles of the Christian life.

DVD Notes

_____
_____
_____
_____
_____

Assignment

I-MAP

As you work with key leaders in your congregation answer the following questions. Also at this time, go to www.L3incubator.com, Session Seven to see examples and ideas of how to focus on spiritual disciplines with leaders in your congregation.

What is the minimum and the maximum commitment to the practice of spiritual disciplines you expect of leaders in your congregation?

_____
_____
_____
_____
_____

What spiritual disciplines do you commit to practicing as a group?

_____
_____
_____
_____
_____

How does your leadership intentionally participate in the worship of God and in service to the community?

_____
_____
_____
_____
_____

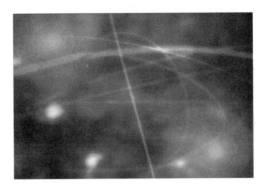

Session Eight

An Environment of Prayer

"Pray then in this way: Our Father in heaven, hallowed be your name. Your kingdom come. Your will be done, on earth as it is in heaven. Give us this day our daily bread. And forgive us our debts, as we also have forgiven our debtors. And do not bring us to the time of trial, but rescue us from the evil one. For if you forgive others their trespasses, your heavenly Father will also forgive you; but if you do not forgive others, neither will your Father forgive your trespasses." MATTHEW 6:9-15

Today's Outline		What You Need to Lead
L¹: Love **Incubate Your Heart** (30 min.) **Formation Que** (90 min.)	**Keys to Prayer**	**DVD: Session Eight** **Incubator Guidebook**
L²: Learn **Reflection** (45 min.)	**Spiritual Disciplines of the Leaders**	**Incubator Guidebook**
Key Concept (60 min.)	**An Environment of Prayer**	**DVD: Session Eight** **www.L3incubator.com** **Session Notes for Session Eight**
L³: Lead **Assignment** (15 min.)		**Incubator Guidebook**

Formation Que

The covenantal question or questions that all L³ Incubator participants agree to answer and be accountable to each time the Incubator meets.

(List names of your Incubator participants below)

_____
_____
_____
_____
_____
_____
_____
_____
_____
_____
_____

"What will I do to live in full devotion to Jesus Christ?"

(List responses below)

_____
_____
_____
_____
_____
_____
_____
_____
_____
_____
_____

Reflection

FOUR BY FOUR (30 MINUTES)

Divide into groups of four and share what you learned from the last session about the practice of spiritual disciplines of you and your leaders.

Write down some of your reflections as you share with one another.

_____
_____
_____
_____

GROUP LEARNING (15 MINUTES)

What are you learning about the practice of spiritual disciplines?

_____
_____
_____

Write down what you have learned about spiritual disciplines from listening to the group.

_____
_____
_____
_____
_____
_____

Key Concept

An Environment of Prayer

The primary goal is to use prayer to prepare a ministry for transformation and bring unity to the common purpose of the ministry. This unity includes not only the leaders of the ministry itself, but also the ministry's response to God's call. If we fail to get this right then the following components of the I-MAP are inconsequential.

Even before the specifics of a new plan are formed, the team preparing the I-MAP must devise ways to hear God and build their trust in God's leading. To be in concert with a spirit of intercession, confession, praise, and dependence on God is to be prepared to plan transformation within a local setting.

The praying church is often the church obsessed with knowing and showing Jesus Christ. This atmosphere and practice is intentionally developed by strategic action of the church leadership and it can begin with the pastor. It is not an afterthought or an addendum ministry. It is vital to all parts of congregational life.

Example strategies for this section of the I-MAP can include items such as:

Intercession prayer for the needs of the community.

Prayer for the leaders preparing the new I-MAP.

Concerts of Prayer to bring all those participating together for corporate prayer.

The formation of special intercessory prayer partners who will pray over difficult decisions and help with discernment.

In later sections of the I-MAP, additional strategies may be developed to further the environment of prayer within a church, such as:

How we initiate new ministry action by praying first.

How to teach children to pray.

How we teach and practice a biblical understanding of prayer.

How we will expose and teach prayer principles, traditions, patterns, and habits.

How we will become a house of prayer for all people.

Deciding what structural changes need to be made to the ministry (organization) to facilitate new values based on prayer.

DVD Notes

_____

_____

_____

_____

_____

Assignment

I-MAP

Begin creating the strategies of prayer that will inform and lead your ministry, the development of your I-MAP, and your Incubator.
How would you typify your church?

Prayerless Church

Prayer Ministry Church

House of Prayer Church

What is the current state of prayer in your church?

_____

_____

_____

In what ways are you training people to pray at all ages and levels of congregational life?

_____

_____

_____

How are people's prayer needs linked to those who pray?

_____

_____

_____

Does prayer fit into your administrative life?

_____

_____

_____

Who prays for the leaders?

_____

_____

_____

Session Nine

Living as Team

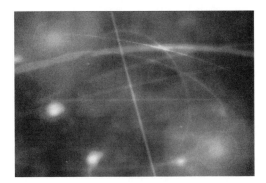

For just as the body is one and has many members, and all the members of the body, though many, are one body, so it is with Christ. For in the one Spirit we were all baptized into one body—Jews or Greeks, slaves or free—and we were all made to drink of one Spirit. Indeed, the body does not consist of one member but of many. 1 CORINTHIANS 12:12-14

Today's Outline

L¹: Love
Incubate Your Heart (30 min.)
Formation Que (90 min.)

Solo or Symphony

L²: Learn
Reflection (45 min.)
Key Concept (60 min.)

Prayer
Team as
Biblical Community

L³: Lead
Assignment (15 min.)

What You Need to Lead

DVD: Session Nine
Incubator Guidebook

Incubator Guidebook
DVD: Session Nine
www.L3incubator.com
Session Notes for Session Nine

Incubator Guidebook

Formation Que

The covenantal question or questions that all L³ Incubator participants agree to answer and be accountable to each time the Incubator meets.

(List names of your Incubator participants below)

"What will I do to live in full devotion to Jesus Christ?"

(List responses below)

Reflection

FOUR BY FOUR (30 MINUTES)

Divide into groups of four and share what you learned about yourself from the last session about the importance of having a prayer strategy.

Write down some of your reflections as you share with one another.

_____

_____

_____

GROUP LEARNING (15 MINUTES)

What are you learning about prayer?

_____

_____

_____

Write down what you have learned about congregational prayer from listening to the group.

_____

_____

_____

_____

_____

Key Concept

Living as Team

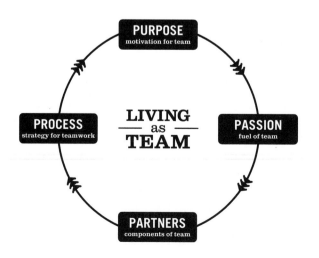

DVD Notes

_____

_____

_____

_____

_____

Assignment
I-MAP

What kind of team would you build if:

Time, Space, Money, . . . resources of any kind didn't matter?

_____

_____

_____

_____

_____

All the rules were laid aside for a few moments?

_____

_____

_____

_____

_____

You could pick anyone in addition to or instead of the people you already have on your team?

_____

_____

_____

_____

_____

Session Ten

Steps to Team Building

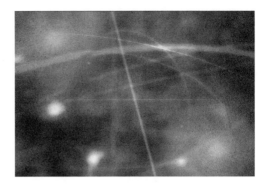

For just as the body is one and has many members, and all the members of the body, though many, are one body, so it is with Christ. 1 CORINTHIANS 12:12

Today's Outline

L[1]: Love
Incubate Your Heart (30 min.)
Formation Que (90 min.)

The Body of Christ

L[2]: Learn
Reflection (45 min.)
Key Concept (60 min.)

Living as Team
Steps to Team Building

L[3]: Lead
Assignment (15 min.)

What You Need to Lead

DVD: Session Ten
Incubator Guidebook

Incubator Guidebook
DVD: Session Ten
www.L3incubator.com
Session Notes for Session Ten

Incubator Guidebook

Formation Que

The covenantal question or questions that all L[3] Incubator participants agree to answer and be accountable to each time the Incubator meets.

(List names of your Incubator participants below)

"What will I do to live in full devotion to Jesus Christ?"

(List responses below)

Reflection

FOUR BY FOUR (30 MINUTES)

Divide into groups of four and share what you learned about yourself from the last session on teams.

Write down some of your reflections as you share with one another.

_____

_____

_____

GROUP LEARNING (15 MINUTES)

What are you learning about team?

_____

_____

_____

Write down what you have learned about teams from listening to the group:

_____

_____

_____

_____

_____

_____

Key Concept

Six Steps to Team Building

Step 1: What are we trying to accomplish? What is the hoped-for outcome?
–How does the outcome complement your values?
–Why? Why? Why? Why? Why?
–Does your outcome help build towards your organization's vision?

Step 2: Name your team(s)
–Trustees, VBS, Worship Team, Creative new teams, etc.

Step 3: Identify the functions needed to operate your team
–Three to seven functions per team
–Functions complement one another

Step 4: Drawing the team diagram
–Place the outcome under the team name
–Create three to seven overlapping circles/ellipses, representing each person
–Label each circle/ellipse above with that team member's function
–Identify the gifts and strengths needed for each circle

Step 5: Identify who needs to be on your team
–For each function, list possible people with the gifts and strengths to serve on this team
–Prioritize

Step 6: Select names of people for each of the areas who would complement that part of the ministry
–Don't forget to consider people who are outside of your current ministry setting
–Prioritize functions needed for the team and invite people accordingly
Concepts from Wayne Corderio, *Doing Church As a Team* (Ventura, CA: Regal Books, 2001).

DVD Notes

_____
_____
_____
_____
_____

Assignment

I-MAP

Using the Six Steps to Team Building, begin to create your team.

If you are not ready to create your team, work with at least two other people to imagine a specific team in your church.

Session Eleven

The Third Place

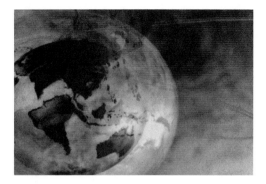

The jailer called for lights, and rushing in, he fell down trembling before Paul and Silas. Then he brought them outside and said, "Sirs, what must I do to be saved?" ACTS 16:29-30

Today's Outline

L¹: Love
Incubate Your Heart (30 min.)   Conversion
Formation Que (90 min.)

L²: Learn
Reflection (45 min.)   Building a Team
Key Concept (60 min.)   The Third Place

L³: Lead
Assignment (15 min.)

What You Need to Lead

DVD: Session Eleven
Incubator Guidebook

Incubator Guidebook
DVD: Session Eleven
www.L3incubator.com
Session Notes for Session Eleven

Incubator Guidebook

Formation Que

The covenantal question or questions that all L³ Incubator participants agree to answer and be accountable to each time the Incubator meets.

(List names of your Incubator participants below)

"What will I do to live in full devotion to Jesus Christ?"

(List responses below)

Reflection

FOUR BY FOUR (30 MINUTES)

Divide into groups of four and share what you learned about building a team.

Write down some of your reflections as you share with one another.

_____
_____
_____
_____

GROUP LEARNING (15 MINUTES)

What are you learning about developing teams?

_____
_____
_____

Write down what you have learned about teams from listening to the group.

_____
_____
_____
_____
_____

Key Concept

Rules for assessing current reality:

No one is to blame.

If there is a hole in the boat, we are all at risk.

The end goal is to move towards a preferred future.

To reach agreement, all who have a stake in the future must participate.

The Third Place

In order to plan for change, a ministry needs to get a picture of current reality. The clearer the picture, the better. There are many tools and resources that can be used, but first there needs to be a willingness to see and learn what is happening in the church. Without a clear picture a ministry cannot develop adequate vision or strategies.

The Third Place is the place between home and work where people gather for meaning and community.

**Today churches compete with many options,
each of which have become "The Third Place."**

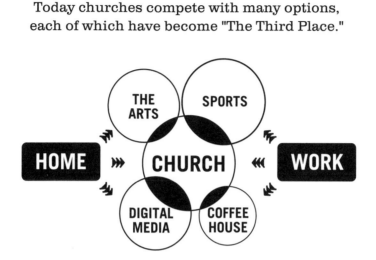

DVD Notes

_____

_____

_____

_____

_____

Assignment

I-MAP

Preparation for Session Fourteen

The focus of Session Fourteen will be on the results of your assessment/discernment tool. You will need to use an assessment/discernment tool like the Church Vitality Indicator with your congregation. Depending on the tool, it can take a month to work through the testing and results. This will need to be done outside of your Incubator sessions.

Use the Church Vitality Indicator booklet that is included with your kit to sign in for your church to access the tools and templates on www.cvindicator.com. If you are using the CVI as your assessment tool, follow the instructions for taking the survey and refining the results. If you are using Natural Church Development, Gallup, or a tool you have developed, follow its instructions so you will have your results ready for Session Fourteen.

Before the next session, visit a Third Place other than a church. (You may have to go more than once.) Answer these questions:

1. How are people finding meaning?

_____

_____

_____

2. How are people creating community?

_____

_____

_____

3. What are their shared values?

_____

_____

_____

4. What is the atmosphere of this Third Place?

_____

_____

_____

a. Why do people return?

_____

_____

_____

b. What makes it distinctive?

_____

_____

_____

c. How would you describe the regulars?

_____

_____

_____

Session Twelve

The Experience-Based Culture

Now when they heard this, they were cut to the heart and said to Peter and the other apostles, "Brothers, what should we do?" Peter said to them, "Repent, and be baptized every one of you in the name of Jesus Christ so that your sins may be forgiven; and you will receive the gift of the Holy Spirit." ACTS 2:37-38

Today's Outline

L¹: Love
Incubate Your Heart (30 min.)
Formation Que (90 min.)

Who is Jesus?
Incubator Guidebook

L²: Learn
Reflection (45 min.)
Key Concept (60 min.)

The Third Place
The Experience-Based
Culture

L³: Lead
Assignment

What You Need to Lead

DVD: Session Twelve

Incubator Guidebook
DVD: Session Twelve
www.L3incubator.com
Session Notes for Session Twelve

Incubator Guidebook

Formation Que

The covenantal question or questions that all L³ Incubator participants agree to answer and be accountable to each time the Incubator meets.

(List names of your Incubator participants below)

"What will I do to live in full devotion to Jesus Christ?"

(List responses below)

Reflection

Four by Four (30 minutes)

Divide into groups of four and share what you learned about your church becoming The Third Place.

Write down some of your reflections as you share with one another.

_____
_____
_____
_____
_____
_____

Group Learning (15 minutes)

What are you learning about the church being an alternative?

_____
_____
_____

Write down what you have learned about context from listening to the group.

_____
_____
_____
_____
_____

Key Concept

The Experience-Based Culture

Today, we live in an experience-based culture. To connect with people, congregations need to create rich experiences of the grace of God to communicate the gospel. This is not entertainment—this is creating environments where mystery and meaning are infused into worship, disciple-making, steward formation, faith-sharing, and prayer.

Out of which framework do you primarily think?
Which way predominates in your church?
What are the implications?
Discuss.

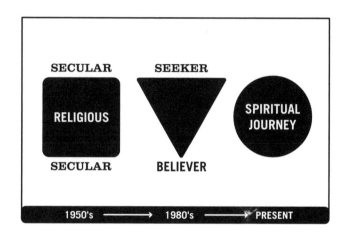

Discuss the plusses and minuses of these two approaches.
What are the implications for ministry?

FACT-BASED	EXPERIENCE-BASED
Bible as Word of God	Bible as Touch Stone
Remembering	Formation
Service	Stewardship
Get it Right	Find Right Path
Job	Vocation
Religion	Spiritual Journey
Rational	Mystery
Vertical	Horizontal

DVD Notes

_____

_____

_____

_____

_____

Assignment

I-MAP

Does your church operate out of a secular/religious, seeker/believer, and/or spiritual journey mindset?

_____

_____

_____

What are the implications of reaching people who live in an experience-based culture? How does this affect your ministry areas? (worship, Christian Education, etc.)

_____

_____

_____

Work on your assessment/discernment survey and results, which need to be ready for Session Fourteen.

_____

_____

_____

_____

_____

Lifecycle of the Church

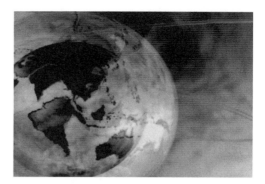

One man was there who had been ill for thirty-eight years. When Jesus saw him lying there and knew that he had been lying there a long time, he said to him, "Do you want to be made well?" JOHN 5:5-6

Today's Outline

L¹: Love
Incubate Your Heart (30 min.)   Bethsada Experience
Formation Que (90 min.)

L²: Learn
Reflection (45 min.)   Experience-Based Culture
Key Concept (60 min.)   Lifecycle of the Church

L³: Lead
Assignment

What You Need to Lead

DVD: Session Thirteen
Incubator Guidebook

Incubator Guidebook
DVD: Session Thirteen
www.L3incubator.com
Session Notes for Session Thirteen

Incubator Guidebook

Formation Que

The covenantal question or questions that all L³ Incubator participants agree to answer and be accountable to each time the Incubator meets.

(List names of your Incubator participants below)

_____
_____
_____
_____
_____
_____
_____
_____
_____
_____
_____

"What will I do to live in full devotion to Jesus Christ?"

(List responses below)

_____
_____
_____
_____
_____
_____
_____
_____
_____
_____
_____

Reflection

FOUR BY FOUR (30 MINUTES)

Divide into groups of four and share what you learned about yourself from the last session about living in an experience-based culture.

Write down some of your reflections as you share with one another.

_____
_____
_____

GROUP LEARNING (15 MINUTES)

What are you discovering about developing experience-based ministries?

_____
_____
_____

Write down your thoughts about what you have learned from listening to the group:

_____
_____

Key Concept

Lifecycle of the Church

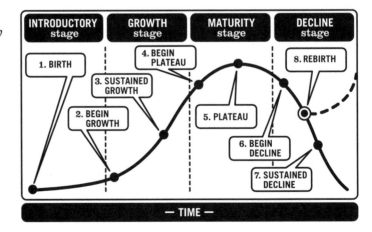

Organizations, as well as churches, go through lifecycles. If you are able to locate yourself on the lifecycle, you can see what steps to take to avoid decline or move into rebirth.

DVD Notes

Assignment

I-MAP

Locate your church on the lifecycle. What challenges and opportunities does this point represent?

Finish your assessment and bring your results to the next session.

Session Fourteen

Assessment Results

Then Jesus told his disciples, "If any want to become my followers, let them deny themselves and take up their cross and follow me." MATTHEW 16:24

Today's Outline		What You Need to Lead
L¹: Love		
Incubate Your Heart (30 min.)	**Four Challenges for the Church**	DVD: Session Fourteen
Formation Que (90 min.)		Incubator Guidebook
L²: Learn		
Reflection (45 min.)	**Lifecycle of the Church**	Incubator Guidebook
Key Concept (60 min.)	**Assessment Results**	DVD: Session Fourteen
		www.L3incubator.com
		Session Notes for Session Fourteen
L³: Lead		
Assignment		Incubator Guidebook

Formation Que

The covenantal question or questions that all L³ Incubator participants agree to answer and be accountable to each time the Incubator meets.

"What will I do to live in full devotion to Jesus Christ?"

(List names of your Incubator participants below)

_____
_____
_____
_____
_____
_____
_____
_____
_____
_____

(List responses below)

_____
_____
_____
_____
_____
_____
_____
_____
_____
_____

Reflection

FOUR BY FOUR (30 MINUTES)

Divide into groups of four and share what you learned about the lifecycle of your church.

Write down some of your reflections as you share with one another.

_____

_____

_____

GROUP LEARNING (15 MINUTES)

What are you learning about the importance of assessing the ministry of your congregation?

_____

_____

_____

Write down your thoughts about current reality that you have learned from listening to the group.

_____

_____

_____

_____

_____

Key Concept

Assessment Results

When listening to the stories of some of the most successful congregations and ministries you will often hear them say, "We learn more from our mistakes than our successes."

Typically, congregations that are mature in their faith have a capacity to evaluate their ministry in ways that allow them to learn rather than to blame. One of the most important shifts in thinking a ministry can make is to become a learning organization, one that seeks to listen deeply so it can respond effectively.

Assessment and discernment tools are useful for identifying current reality. They are a starting point for further reflection, discussion, and research. They are not the answer. They allow the fun to begin—to pray and listen to the voice of God that stirs in our hearts, a voice that calls us forward to be in ministry with those who surround us.

With your group, review the results of your Assessment (CVI, NCD, or other tool). As you review the results keep the following in mind:

No one is to blame.

The assessment is a snapshot in time. Repeated use over time will enable you to track improvement.

Look for potential ways to improve, asking the following questions: What is going well? What have you learned? What needs improvement?

DVD Notes

_____

_____

_____

_____

_____

_____

Assignment
I-MAP

Review the information you have gathered over the last four sessions dealing with context and ask the following:

1. What is going well?

_____

_____

_____

2. What have you learned?

_____

_____

_____

3. What needs to be improved?

_____

_____

_____

4. Where do you find the greatest potential for being in ministry with new people?

_____

_____

_____

Session Fifteen

Vision Overview

Therefore, since we are surrounded by so great a cloud of witnesses, let us also lay aside every weight and the sin that clings so closely, and let us run with perseverance the race that is set before us, looking to Jesus the pioneer and perfecter of our faith, who for the sake of the joy that was set before him endured the cross, disregarding its shame, and has taken his seat at the right hand of the throne of God. HEBREWS 12:1-2

Today's Outline		What You Need to Lead
L¹: Love		
Incubate Your Heart (30 min.)	**Seeing the Invisible**	**DVD: Session Fifteen**
Formation Que (90 min.)		**Incubator Guidebook**
L²: Learn		
Reflection (45 min.)	**Assessment Results**	**Incubator Guidebook**
Key Concept (60 min.)	**Vision Overview**	**DVD: Session Fifteen**
		www.L3incubator.com
		Session Notes for Session Fifteen
L³: Lead		
Assignment (15 min.)		**Incubator Guidebook**

Formation Que

The covenantal question or questions that all L³ Incubator participants agree to answer and be accountable to each time the Incubator meets.

(List names of your Incubator participants below)

"What will I do to live in full devotion to Jesus Christ?"

< Remember >
(List responses below)
- Only Holy Spirit can bring transformation.
- Respect for every individual in the group
- Leaders are called to gently yet firmly apply means of accountability
- We are to fix one another (not heal)
- Answer in first person.

Reflection

FOUR BY FOUR (30 MINUTES)

Share what you learned from getting a picture of your congregation's current reality.

Write down some of your reflections as you share with one another.

_____

_____

_____

GROUP LEARNING (15 MINUTES)

Where do you find the greatest potential for being in ministry with new people?

_____

_____

_____

Write down what you have learned from listening to the group.

_____

_____

_____

_____

_____

_____

Key Concept

Vision Overview

STRATEGY

The tasks or activities that help us live out the vision.

VISION

Our picture of the future that we head toward.

MISSION

What we do.

VALUES

The beliefs or convictions that underlie our vision and mission.

DEFINE

STRATEGY

We will do...

VISION

We see...

MISSION

We are called to...

VALUES

We believe...

DEFINE

STRATEGY

DEVISE a strategic plan that will grow the vision over time.

VISION

DESCRIBE in a word-picture what the full-grown dream looks like.
DELINEATE threats to the vision.

MISSION

DECLARE in a phrase or sentence your reason for being. Make sure it's easy to remember.

VALUES

DISCOVER the deeply held beliefs that are roots.
DEFINE your "non-negotiable" (those things about which there is no compromise).

DEFINE

STRATEGY

What actions are you willing to take to live out the strategy?

VISION

Are you willing to give your life to the corporate vision?

MISSION

Is your life mission consistent with the corporate mission?

VALUES

Are your personal values consistent with the values of your faith community?

DEFINE

STRATEGY

We are committed to...

VISION

The vision of our Church is...

MISSION

We are called to...

VALUES

Our congregational values are...

DEFINE

* Draw a picture respresenting Vision

STRATEGY

REVIEW constantly. Are we doing what it takes to get there?
REPORT on progress toward the vision.
REORGANIZE if necessary to live out the vision.

VISION

REFOCUS on what the future looks like based on the vision.
RENEW commitment to the right direction.
REVISIT your context to see if you are on target.

MISSION

REMIND people constantly what business you are in.
REMEMBER why you are doing what you are doing.

VALUES

REALIGN your values constantly. Drift happens.
RESTATE your values often.
RECLAIM your values through new people.
REVIVE your values through self-examination.

DEFINE

Assignment

I-MAP

Research the value statements of two effective churches and report on them for the next session.

Session Sixteen

Congregational Values

Or don't you know that your body is a temple of the Holy Spirit within you, which you have from God, and that you are not your own? 1 CORINTHIANS 6:19

Today's Outline

L¹: Love
Incubate Your Heart (30 min.)

Formation Que (90 min.)

L²: Learn
Reflection (45 min.)
Key Concept (60 min.)

L³: Lead
Assignment (15 min.)

Building a House of Prayer

Vision Overview
Congregational Values

What You Need to Lead

DVD: Session Sixteen

Incubator Guidebook

Incubator Guidebook
DVD: Session Sixteen
www.L3incubator.com
Session Notes for Session Sixteen

Incubator Guidebook

Formation Que

The covenantal question or questions that all L³ Incubator participants agree to answer and be accountable to each time the Incubator meets.

(List names of your Incubator participants below)

"What will I do to live in full devotion to Jesus Christ?"

(List responses below)

Reflection

FOUR BY FOUR (30 MINUTES)

Divide into groups of four and share what you learned about the values of leading congregations.

Write down some of your reflections as you share with one another.

_____
_____
_____

GROUP LEARNING (15 MINUTES)

What are you learning about congregational values?

_____
_____
_____

Write down what you have learned from listening to the group.

_____
_____
_____
_____
_____

Key Concept

Congregational Values

Core values are unwritten ideas, traditions, and rules that underlie everything that happens.

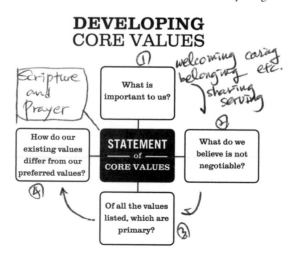

DEVELOPING CORE VALUES

DVD Notes

_____
_____
_____
_____

Assignment

I-MAP

Using the Vision Overview templates found in Session Fifteen, answer the questions related to values. Focus on answering, "Our congregational values are…"

_____
_____
_____
_____
_____
_____
_____
_____
_____
_____
_____
_____

- Values are foundations of:
  - vision
  - mission
  - Strategic planning

e.g. Jesus with disciples : 3 years of values.

Core values

e.g.
- Dress code is one of core values

- every thing could communicate core values.
  reflect

- unwritten ideas. traditions and rules that underlie every thing that happens.

- The ability to move into the future is often times closely tied with the willingness to discover core values and to evaluate them in light of current reality of the congregation.

• mission and purpose are interchangeable words.

⇓

THINK VERBS, (not nouns)

✳ what are the 3-5 ~~too~~ most basic steps to doing what you do?

engage → relate

serve ↑ ↓ equip

Session Seventeen

Vision & Mission

And I pray that Christ will be more and more at home in your hearts as you trust in him. May your roots go down deep into the soil of God's marvelous love. And may you have the power to understand, as all God's people should, how wide, how long, how high, and how deep his love really is. EPHESIANS 3:17-19 (NLT)

Today's Outline

L¹: Love
Incubate Your Heart (30 min.)

Formation Que (90 min.)

L²: Learn
Reflection (45 min.)
Key Concept (60 min.)

L³: Lead
Assignment (15 min.)

Living the Realm
of Possibility

Congregational Values
Vision & Mission

What You Need to Lead

DVD: Session Seventeen

Incubator Guidebook

Incubator Guidebook
DVD: Session Seventeen
www.L3incubator.com
Session Notes for Session Seventeen

Incubator Guidebook

Formation Que

The covenantal question or questions that all L³ Incubator participants agree to answer and be accountable to each time the Incubator meets.

(List names of your Incubator participants below)

"What will I do to live in full devotion to Jesus Christ?"

(List responses below)

Reflection

FOUR BY FOUR (30 MINUTES)

Divide into groups of four and share about the values of your congregation.

Write down some of your reflections as you share with one another.

_____
_____
_____
_____

GROUP LEARNING (15 MINUTES)

What are you learning about values?

_____
_____
_____

Write down what you have learned from listening to the group.

_____
_____
_____
_____

Key Concept

Vision & Mission

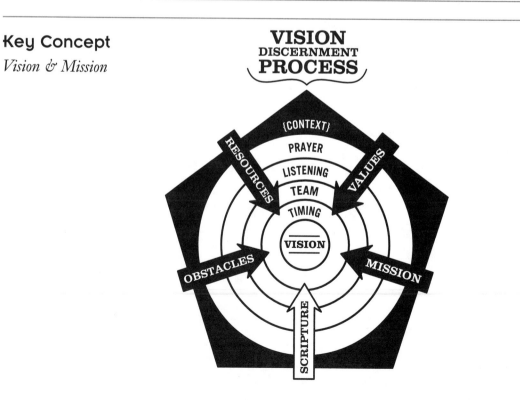

DVD Notes

_____

_____

_____

_____

Assignment

I-MAP

Using the Vision Template in Session Fifteen, answer the questions concerning Mission and Vision.

_____

_____

_____

Focus on these two questions:

(Mission) We are called to…

_____

_____

_____

(Vision) The vision of our church is…

_____

_____

_____

Session Eighteen

Sustaining the Vision

He said to them, "Cast the net to the right side of the boat, and you will find some." So they cast it, and now they were not able to haul it in because there were so many fish.
JOHN 21:6

Today's Outline

L¹: Love
Incubate Your Heart (30 min.)
Formation Que (90 min.)

Whose side are you on?

L²: Learn
Reflection (45 min.)
Key Concept (60 min.)

Vision & Mission
Sustaining the Vision

L³: Lead
Assignment (15 min.)

What You Need to Lead

DVD: Session Eighteen
Incubator Guidebook

Incubator Guidebook
DVD: Session Eighteen
www.L3incubator.com
Session Notes for Session Eighteen

Incubator Guidebook

Formation Que

The covenantal question or questions that all L³ Incubator participants agree to answer and be accountable to each time the Incubator meets.

(List names of your Incubator participants below)

"What will I do to live in full devotion to Jesus Christ?"

(List responses below)

Reflection

Share how you answered the two questions about Vision and Mission.
We are called to…
The vision of our church is…

Write down some of your reflections as you share with one another.

_____

_____

_____

_____

_____

_____

What are you learning about Vision and Mission?

_____

_____

_____

Write down your thoughts from listening to the group:

_____

_____

_____

_____

_____

_____

_____

_____

Key Concept

Sustaining the Vision

Three pointers on how to sustain vision:
1. Cast the Vision:
   Identify the problem
   State the solution to the problem
   Identify "why you" and "why now" the solution should happen.

2.   Celebrate the Vision
     Strategically plan to celebrate the realization of the Vision as it happens on a daily basis. Identifying transformation in people has a far greater impact than saying "you should transform."

3.   Live the Vision
     The most important aspect of casting a compelling vision is to demonstrate it with your life.

Andy Stanley, *Vision Leak: Cast, Celebrate, and Live It.* Main Session, Willow Creek Community Church Leadership Summit, August 7-9, 2003.

DVD Notes

_____

_____

_____

_____

_____

Assignment

I-MAP

Look over your values, mission, and vision statements to further refine them. Ask people outside the Incubator the following:
>   Are they clear?
>   Are they biblically based?
>   Are they easy to remember?
>   Do they reflect your assessment of current reality?
>   What are the potential stumbling blocks?

Designing a system
- determine the most important longterm results.
- Start with the finish

. establish categories to flow.
. give definition to each cate

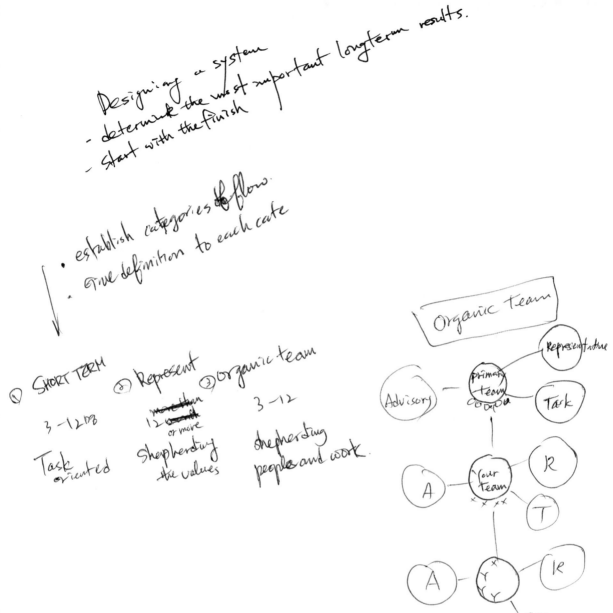

① SHORT TERM   ② Represent   ③ Organic team

3 - 12 08   12 or more   3 - 12

Task oriented   Shepherding   Shepherding
                   the values   people and work.

Organic Team

Introduction to Strategy & Systems

Do not be conformed to this world, but be transformed by the renewing of your minds, so that you may discern what is the will of God—what is good and acceptable and perfect. ROMANS 12:2

Today's Outline

L¹: Love
Incubate Your Heart (30 min.)
Formation Que (90 min.)

Why Be Normal?

L²: Learn
Reflection (45 min.)
Key Concept (60 min.)

Sustaining Vision
Introduction to
Strategy & Systems

L³: Lead
Assignment (15 min.)

What You Need to Lead

DVD: Session Nineteen
Incubator Guidebook

Incubator Guidebook
DVD: Session Nineteen
www.L3incubator.com
Session Notes for Session Nineteen

Incubator Guidebook

Formation Que

The covenantal question or questions that all L³ Incubator participants agree to answer and be accountable to each time the Incubator meets.

(List names of your Incubator participants below)

"What will I do to live in full devotion to Jesus Christ?"

(List responses below)

_____   _____
_____   _____

Reflection

FOUR BY FOUR (30 MINUTES)

Review your values, mission, and vision.

Write down some of your reflections as you share with one another.

_____
_____
_____
_____
_____
_____

GROUP LEARNING (15 MINUTES)

What are you learning about sustaining vision?

_____
_____
_____

Write down what you have learned about sustaining vision from listening to the group.

_____
_____
_____
_____
_____
_____
_____
_____

Key Concept

Using the Strategy Template

Use the following templates to discover and redesign your overall congregation system.

《Disciple making Church》
STRATEGY TEMPLATE
— for —
OVERALL SYSTEM

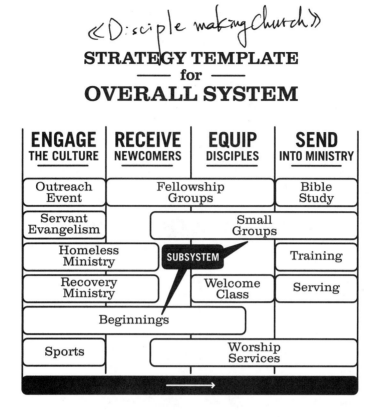

ENGAGE THE CULTURE	RECEIVE NEWCOMERS	EQUIP DISCIPLES	SEND INTO MINISTRY
Outreach Event	Fellowship Groups		Bible Study
Servant Evangelism	Small Groups		
Homeless Ministry	SUBSYSTEM	Training	
Recovery Ministry		Welcome Class	Serving
Beginnings			
Sports	Worship Services		

STRATEGY
STEP ONE

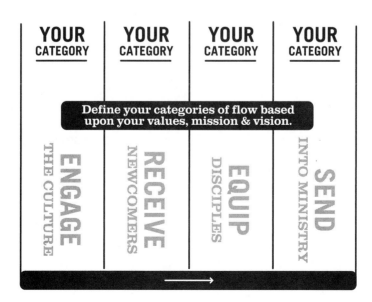

YOUR CATEGORY	YOUR CATEGORY	YOUR CATEGORY	YOUR CATEGORY
ENGAGE THE CULTURE	RECEIVE NEWCOMERS	EQUIP DISCIPLES	SEND INTO MINISTRY

Define your categories of flow based upon your values, mission & vision.

STRATEGY
STEP TWO

YOUR CATEGORY	YOUR CATEGORY	YOUR CATEGORY	YOUR CATEGORY

Give definitions for each of the columns.

Ministries that...(for example, help us build relationships with those outside the church and...)	Ministries that...	Ministries that...	Ministries that...

DVD Notes

Assignment

I-MAP

Using Strategy Step One, refine your categories of flow based upon your values, mission, and vision.

Using Strategy Step Two, refine definitions for each of the columns.

Measurement

He said to them, "Is a lamp brought in to be put under the bushel basket, or under the bed, and not on the lampstand? For there is nothing hidden, except to be disclosed; nor is anything secret, except to come to light. Let anyone with ears to hear listen!" And he said to them, "Pay attention to what you hear; the measure you give will be the measure you get, and still more will be given you. For to those who have, more will be given; and from those who have nothing, even what they have will be taken away." MARK 4:21-25

Today's Outline		What You Need to Lead
L¹: Love		
Incubate Your Heart (30 min.)		**DVD: Session Twenty**
Formation Que (90 min.)		**Incubator Guidebook**
L²: Learn		
Reflection (45 min.)	Introduction to Strategy & Systems	**Incubator Guidebook**
Key Concept (60 min.)	Measurement	**DVD: Session Twenty** www.L3incubator.com **Session Notes for Session Twenty**
L³: Lead		
Assignment (15 min.)		**Incubator Guidebook**

Formation Que

The covenantal question or questions that all L³ Incubator participants agree to answer and be accountable to each time the Incubator meets.

(List names of your Incubator participants below)

"What will I do to live in full devotion to Jesus Christ?"

(List responses below)

Reflection

FOUR BY FOUR (30 MINUTES)

Share your categories of flow and your definitions for each of the columns in the strategy template.

Write down some of your reflections as you share with one another.

_____
_____
_____

GROUP LEARNING (15 MINUTES)

What are you learning about systems?

_____
_____
_____

Write down your thoughts from listening to the group:

_____
_____
_____
_____
_____
_____

Key Concept

Measurement

Measurement
- Definition
  - The review of the results of a ministry or task as compared to a standard.
- Rationale
  - Gives you the ability to assess current reality in order to create strategies that will move you into the future.

Depending on the situation, one style of leadership may be more effective.

ADAPTIVE STYLE
— VS —
TECHNICAL STYLE

ADAPTIVE	TECHNICAL
Learning & developing strategies together.	Identify, organize & distribute tasks for completion.
Use white board or similar tools to capture thoughts & ideas.	Write down who is responsible for each task.
Encourage healthy conflict.	Set time frames for completion.
Discourage the temptation to bring the conversation to a close prematurely.	Identify what results each task should produce.

DVD Notes

_____

_____

_____

_____

Assignment

I-MAP

Fill out Strategy Step Three as you create measurements for each category.

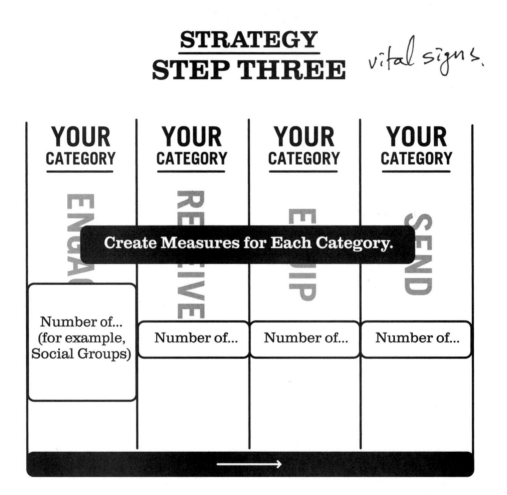

Session Twenty-One

Priorities

My soul yearns for you in the night, my spirit within me earnestly seeks you. ISAIAH 26:9

Today's Outline		What You Need to Lead
L^1: Love		
Incubate Your Heart (30 min.)	**Desire**	**DVD: Session Twenty-one**
Formation Que (90 min.)		**Incubator Guidebook**
L^2: Learn		
Reflection (45 min.)	**Measurement**	**Incubator Guidebook**
Key Concept (60 min.)	**Priorities**	**DVD: Session Twenty-one**
		www.L3incubator.com
		Session Notes for Session Twenty-one
L^3: Lead		
Assignment (15 min.)		**Incubator Guidebook**

Formation Que

The covenantal question or questions that all L^3 Incubator participants agree to answer and be accountable to each time the Incubator meets.

(List names of your Incubator participants below)

"What will I do to live in full devotion to Jesus Christ?"

(List responses below)

Reflection

FOUR BY FOUR (30 MINUTES)

Share your Measurements for each category.

Write down some of your reflections as you share with one another.

_____

_____

GROUP LEARNING (15 MINUTES)

What are you learning about Measurement?

_____

_____

_____

Write down what you have learned about Measurements from listening to the group.

_____

_____

_____

_____

Key Concept

Priorities

STRATEGIC PRIORITIES — TABLE —

ASSESSMENT RESULTS {END OF CHAPTER 14}	STRATEGIES THAT YOU BELIEVE WILL AFFECT CHANGE {NEW OR EXISTING}	PRIORITY {WHERE DO YOU START FIRST?}
Experiential Worship		
	Ancient Future	2
	Morning Communion	5
	11am Sunday Service	4
Biblical Literacy		
	Disciple Bible Study	1
	Beginnings	3

STRATEGY
STEP FOUR *Existing Ministries*

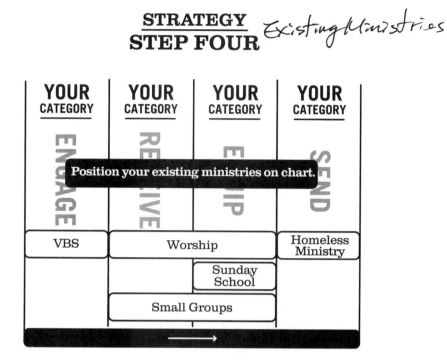

STRATEGY
STEP FIVE *New Ministries*

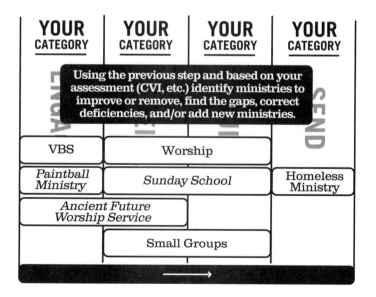

DVD Notes

Assignment

I-MAP

1. Using the Strategic Priorities Table, place your assessment results and begin looking at possible strategies.

2. Use Strategy Step Four to position your existing ministries on the chart.

3. Using the previous steps and based upon your assessment (CVI, etc.), use Strategy Step Five and identify ministries to improve or remove, find the gaps, correct deficiencies, and/or add new ministries.

Structure

They devoted themselves to the apostles' teaching and fellowship, to the breaking of bread and the prayers. ACTS 2:42

Today's Outline

L¹: Love
Incubate Your Heart (30 min.)   One Plus Many
Formation Que (90 min.)

L²: Learn
Reflection (45 min.)   Priorities
Key Concept (60 min.)   Structures

L³: Lead
Take-home Assignment (15 min.)

What You Need to Lead

DVD: Session Twenty-two
Incubator Guidebook

Incubator Guidebook
DVD: Session Twenty-two
www.L3incubator.com
Session Notes for Session Twenty-two

Incubator Guidebook

Formation Que

The covenantal question or questions that all L³ Incubator participants agree to answer and be accountable to each time the Incubator meets.

(List names of your Incubator participants below)

"What will I do to live in full devotion to Jesus Christ?"

(List responses below)

Reflection

FOUR BY FOUR (30 MINUTES)

Share Steps Four & Five from your Strategy templates.

Write down some of your reflections as you share with one another.

_____
_____
_____

GROUP LEARNING (15 MINUTES)

What are you learning about setting priorities?

_____
_____
_____

Write down your thoughts from listening to the group.

_____
_____
_____
_____
_____
_____

Key Concept

Structures

Introduction to Structures

- Structure provides the framework in which relationships are connected.
- Rigid structures provide control.
- Flexible structures can change and adapt easily.
- Clear structures allow people to work with confidence.
- Hierarchical structures allow people to know who they are responsible for and to.

Organizations that meet the needs of their constituents and build for the future have structures that match their values, mission, and vision.

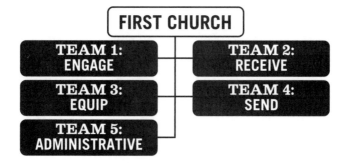

Using Strategy Step Six, think about ways
your structure echoes your categories.
Some congregations organize themselves
around the major categories.

Go to L3incubator.com for more examples.

STRATEGY
STEP SIX   *Feeds*

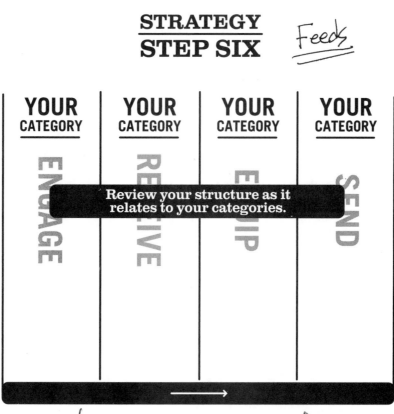

*How does each ministry receive people from the previous category
and how does each ministry send people to the next ministry?*

DVD Notes

_____

_____

_____

_____

_____

Assignment

I-MAP

Using Strategy Step Six, continue to review your structure as it relates to your categories.

STEP SEVEN.

→ Once a general understanding of your system
is in place, next & critical step is to establish
how leaders share the responsibility.
Establish relational connections and boundaries.

→ relational connections.
① Def. = the framework on which relationships are connected.
② Rigid connections and boundaries provide control.
③ Flexible   "   can & change and easily adapt

Session Twenty-Three

Structure & Systems Review

Then the LORD said to Noah, "Go into the ark, you and all your household, for I have seen that you alone are righteous before me in this generation." GENESIS 7:1

Today's Outline		What You Need to Lead
L¹: Love		
Incubate Your Heart (30 min.)	**Mandate for**	DVD: Session Twenty-three
	Leadership	Incubator Guidebook
Formation Que (90 min.)		
L²: Learn		
Reflection (45 min.)	**Structure**	Incubator Guidebook
Key Concept (60 min.)	**Structure &**	DVD: Session Twenty-three
	Systems Review	
		www.L3incubator.com
		Session Notes for Session Twenty-three
L³: Lead		
Assignment (15 min.)		Incubator Guidebook

Formation Que

The covenantal question or questions that all L³ Incubator participants agree to answer and be accountable to each time the Incubator meets.

"What will I do to live in full devotion to Jesus Christ?"

(List names of your Incubator participants below)

(List responses below)

_____

_____

_____

_____

_____

_____

_____

_____

_____

_____

_____

_____

_____

Reflection

FOUR BY FOUR (30 MINUTES)

Talk about how your structure relates to your categories from session nineteen.

Write down some of your reflections as you share with one another.

_____

_____

_____

GROUP LEARNING (15 MINUTES)

What are you learning about structure?

_____

_____

_____

Write down what you have learned about structure from listening to the group.

_____

_____

_____

_____

Key Concept

Structure & Systems Review

Create a chart that contains
each of your categories.

Establish column headings that
help evaluate each strategy.

Give each strategy a sequential
number to prioritize the order
of implementation.

**PRIORITY
CHART**

STRATEGY	DOABILITY	VALUE TO MISSION	COST, TIME, RESOURCES	PRIORITY

DVD Notes

_____

_____

_____

_____

_____

Assignment

I-MAP

Continue to review your structure and prioritize using the priority chart.

Multiplication & Evaluation

When he saw the crowds, he had compassion for them, because they were harassed and helpless, like sheep without a shepherd. Then he said to his disciples, "The harvest is plentiful, but the laborers are few; therefore ask the Lord of the harvest to send out laborers into his harvest." MATTHEW 9:36-38

Today's Outline

L¹: Love
Incubate Your Heart (30 min.)

Formation Que (90 min.)

L²: Learn
Reflection (45 min.)

Key Concept (60 min.)

L³: Lead
Assignment (15 min.)

Remember the Harvest

Strategy & Systems Review
Multiplication & Evaluation

What You Need to Lead

DVD: Session Twenty-four

Incubator Guidebook

Incubator Guidebook

DVD: Session Twenty-four
www.L3incubator.com
Session Notes for Session Twenty-four

Incubator Guidebook

Formation Que

The covenantal question or questions that all L³ Incubator participants agree to answer and be accountable to each time the Incubator meets.

(List names of your Incubator participants below)

"What will I do to live in full devotion to Jesus Christ?"

(List responses below)

Reflection

FOUR BY FOUR (30 MINUTES)

Update the group on your strategy and systems.

Write down some of your reflections as you work with one another.

_____

_____

_____

GROUP LEARNING (15 MINUTES)

What are you learning about strategy and systems?

_____

_____

_____

Write down what you have learned from listening to the group.

_____

_____

_____

_____

_____

_____

Key Concept

Multiplication & Evaluation

Progress is never made without evaluation. People learn as much from failures as they do from successes. Congregations who take seriously the need for constant improvement are not afraid to look carefully at all areas of ministry to see how they can improve.

Leaders replicate themselves. They create systems and strategies for bringing up the next generation of leaders. A true measure of success is what happens after they leave. Is what they started sustained by those who follow?

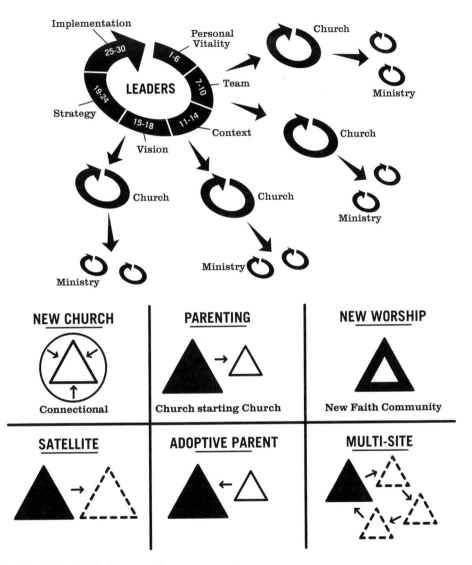

Models of New Faith Communities

A faith community is formed when a worship experience is linked with a discipleship system. A church can offer worship, but if no new people join, it is not a faith community. A church can offer a great youth program or Bible study, but if the participants do not attend worship, they are not part of the faith community.

When a church offers multiple worship experiences, it is leading multiple faith communities. There are a variety of ways that new faith communities can be created.

First is the connectional new church start. This happens when a denomination sponsors a brand-new church and supports the start with a variety of resources.

Second is the Church—starting Church. In this model an existing church provides the resources and leadership to start a new church that will become independent.

Third is the New Worshiping Faith Community. This new faith community is created when a new worship experience and its accompanying discipleship system is offered within the existing facilities of a congregation.

Fourth is the Satellite. In this model a faith community is created off campus of the existing church with the intention that it will remain connected to the existing church.

Fifth is the Adoptive Parent model in which a strong existing church becomes responsible for a neighboring church that is in decline or about to be closed.

Sixth is the Multiple-Site congregation where, under the umbrella of one church, multiple faith communities operate in a variety of sites in the community.

DVD Notes

_____
_____
_____
_____
_____

Assignment

I-MAP

1. Which of your ministries is best posed for multiplication?

_____
_____
_____

2. Practice using the evaluation questions:

- WHAT is the goal?

_____
_____
_____

- SO WHAT is your strategy?

_____
_____
_____

- NOW WHAT are your results?

_____
_____

Implementation
Sessions

During the next six sessions you will be gathering to update each other on the creation of Incubators and to encourage one another in your spiritual growth. This is a critical phase of the Incubator process because it gives you a group of peers to support you as you try new things and institute change.

You will need to have members of the group take turns leading the Incubate Your Heart portion of the session. You can use Incubate Your Heart sections from previous sessions or create your own.

In Session Thirty you may use the Closing Communion Service found on DVD Session Thirty.

Implementation

Today's Outline

L¹: Love
Incubate Your Heart (30 min.)

Formation Que (90 min.)

L²: Learn
Incubator Updates (105 min.)

L³: Lead
Assignment (15 min.)

Develop your own, or use favorites from the past year.

Implementation   **Incubator Guidebook**

Formation Que

The covenantal question or questions that all L³ Incubator participants agree to answer and be accountable to each time the Incubator meets.

(List names of your Incubator participants below)

"What will I do to live in full devotion to Jesus Christ?"

(List responses below)

Icubator Updates

Assignment

Implementation

Have members of your Incubator share the development of their I-MAP and the development of the Incubators they are starting.

Implementation

Today's Outline

L¹: Love
Incubate Your Heart (30 min.)

Develop your own, or use favorites from the past year.

Formation Que (90 min.)

L²: Learn
Incubator Updates (105 min.)

L³: Lead
Assignment (15 min.)   **Implementation**   **Incubator Guidebook**

Formation Que

The covenantal question or questions that all L³ Incubator participants agree to answer and be accountable to each time the Incubator meets.

(List names of your Incubator participants below)

"What will I do to live in full devotion to Jesus Christ?"

(List responses below)

_____

_____

_____

_____

_____

_____

_____

_____

_____

_____

_____

_____

_____

_____

_____

_____

_____

_____

_____

_____

Icubator Updates

Assignment

Implementation

Have members of your Incubator share the development of their I-MAP and the development of the Incubators they are starting.

Implementation

Formation Que

The covenantal question or questions that all L³ Incubator participants agree to answer and be accountable to each time the Incubator meets.

(List names of your Incubator participants below)

"What will I do to live in full devotion to Jesus Christ?"

(List responses below)

Icubator Updates

Assignment

Implementation

Have members of your Incubator share the development of their I-MAP and the development of the Incubators they are starting.

Implementation

Today's Outline

L¹: Love
Incubate Your Heart (30 min.)

Develop your own, or use favorites from the past year.

Formation Que (90 min.)

L²: Learn
Incubator Updates (105 min.)

L³: Lead
Assignment (15 min.)   Implementation   Incubator Guidebook

Formation Que

The covenantal question or questions that all L³ Incubator participants agree to answer and be accountable to each time the Incubator meets.

"What will I do to live in full devotion to Jesus Christ?"

(List names of your Incubator participants below)

(List responses below)

Icubator Updates

Assignment

Implementation

Have members of your Incubator share the development of their I-MAP and the development of the Incubators they are starting.

Session Twenty-Nine
Implementation

Formation Que

The covenantal question or questions
that all L³ Incubator participants agree
to answer and be accountable to each
time the Incubator meets.

(List names of your Incubator participants below)

"What will I do to live in full
devotion to Jesus Christ?"

(List responses below)

_____

_____

_____

_____

_____

_____

_____

_____

_____

_____

_____

_____

_____

_____

_____

_____

_____

_____

_____

_____

Icubator Updates

Assignment

Implementation

Have members of your Incubator share the development of their I-MAP and the development of the
Incubators they are starting.

Session Thirty

Implementation

Today's Outline

L¹: Love
Incubate Your Heart (30 min.)

Formation Que (90 min.)

L³: Lead
Assignment
Closing worship (90 min.)

Implementation
Lasting Hope

Develop your own, or use favorites from the past year.

Incubator Guidebook
DVD Session Thirty

Formation Que

The covenantal question or questions that all L³ Incubator participants agree to answer and be accountable to each time the Incubator meets.

(List names of your Incubator participants below)

_____
_____
_____
_____
_____
_____
_____
_____
_____
_____
_____

"What will I do to live in full devotion to Jesus Christ?"

(List responses below)

_____
_____
_____
_____
_____
_____
_____
_____
_____
_____
_____

Assignment

Implementation

Talk over the following:

How will you continue to be in accountability with others?

_____
_____
_____

What has changed for you during this season of your life?

_____
_____
_____

What key learnings will you continue to apply?

_____
_____
_____

About the Authors:

Barry Carpenter is the Lead Pastor of Immanuel United Methodist Church in Northern Kentucky. He is the former Director of New Church and Congregational Development for the Kentucky Conference.

Craig Kennet Miller is the Director of the Center for Evangelism through New Congregational Development at The General Board of Discipleship of the United Methodist Church. He is the author of numerous books, including *NextChurch.Now: Creating New Faith Communities* and coauthor of *Making God Real for a New Generation*, both published by Discipleship Resources.

Craig W. Robertson is the founding member and Executive Director of Spiritual Leadership, Inc., formerly Chairman of the Board and CEO of Otega Services, Inc., National Technical Director of Odgen, Inc., and founder and President of Lightpath, Inc. Craig is a Lay Pastor and active member of St. Luke United Methodist Church in Lexington Kentucky. craig.r@spiritual-leadership.org